One Bed, One Bank Account *Workbook*

BETTER CONVERSATIONS
ON MONEY AND MARRIAGE

Derek and Carrie Olsen

One Bed, One Bank Account

WORKBOOK EDITION

First Edition, May 2015

Beatnik Publishing

Kansas City, MO

Editor – Mike Loomis

Cover – Banner Services, LLC

Formatting – Carrie Olsen

www.DerekAndCarrie.com

Disclaimer of accountability:

One Bed, One Bank Account and all other works under said name are works of entertainment and should not be considered a substitute for legal or financial advice of any kind. Any and all results, positive or negative, realized from taking action based on the content of this work are the responsibility of the acting party.

One Bed, One Bank Account **WORKBOOK** edition ISBN - 9780985886349

Also available:

One Bed, One Bank Account

Book edition (non-workbook) and audiobook

DerekAndCarrie.com

10 9 4 6 5 8 3 7 2

We recommend reading the book, *One Bed One Bank Account*, before diving in to this workbook!

Available at DerekAndCarrie.com/products

Video instructional series available at derekandcarrie.com/budgetlesson
The video series covers how each worksheet works in greater detail.

CONTENTS

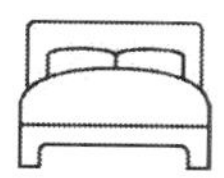

INTRODUCTION

When Carrie and I were newly married, we spent more time than I'd like to admit working through our finances. Not because we were type-A budget freaks with nothing else to do. It was because our circumstances forced it. Just to keep us afloat, we researched dozens of methods and tactics for successfully managing finances. We spent hours looking over spreadsheets, notes and handwritten budgets. It was hard. But now, on the other side of financial disaster, we see that it was so worth it.

I suppose you could call all those months of crazed budgeting, research for this workbook. To save you the drudgery of weeding through the vast abyss of budget tools available, we've corralled all of the most helpful resources that we discovered or developed ourselves and wrapped them up in this little collection you're reading here.

We're glad you've started reading this workbook. And we're glad the word "workbook" didn't deter you from picking it up. We promise this will be nothing like the busy work you were forced to complete in high school. In fact, we think you'll be surprised by how non-workbooky this workbook is.

Naturally, there will be worksheets that will encourage you to think about your finances and your relationship. Many of them will be most helpful to you if you write in your thoughts or fill in the blanks. But there will be others that will call upon your critical thinking skills, or even your artsy, creative side to try and build a more complete picture of your unique situation.

We have found this whole picture approach to be the most beneficial – and the most fun – way to approach the topic of conversations on money and marriage.

The *One Bed, One Bank Account Workbook* is designed to help couples navigate the mechanics and the mindset of combining bank accounts, creating a monthly budget, and establishing a sustainable financial-lifestyle.

Managing your money is a life-long event. If it takes a few weeks to complete this workbook, that's fine. If it takes a few months, that's okay too!

The numbers and math are important for creating your financial plan, but the conversations that come up along the way are the real results we are shooting for.

So, take it slow. Let these pages guide your thoughts, and don't rush the conversations that come up. Instead, let them do the work of fully restoring your financial relationship – one conversation at a time.

Be sure to spend adequate time talking through each worksheet – even if the talks take up more time than actually finishing the worksheet. Creating space and opportunities for you and your spouse to talk about how money shapes your relationship is the real goal of this workbook.

Good conversations about money lead to good money management. We need both to move the ball forward.

How to use this workbook

Each worksheet has a similar design to establish a consistent flow throughout the workbook. This makes it easier and quicker for you to engage each worksheet.

The design is split into three parts:

> **Actionable:** The math and numbers side of the process.
>
> **Better Conversations:** Discussion questions to help you explore how each area of finance affects your relationship.
>
> **Motivational:** A quick shot of motivation. Let's face it we all need a little encouragement in the finance department every now and then.

This process works best when you work through each worksheet *together as a couple.*

Let the conversations enrich your relationship, and let the numbers enrich your bank account!

-Derek and Carrie

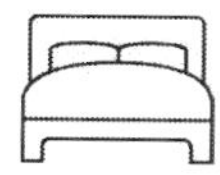

1 Debt Destruction

Debt sucks. But it's nothing to be afraid of or shy away from. If you and your spouse or fiancé have debt, we are pumped about how much better you'll both feel – and how much your finances will improve – when you create a simple plan to get rid of it. We know dealing with debt can be daunting and even feel overwhelming, so we hope that you feel encouraged by taking the first step. Chances are you'll see and feel progress soon; let those feelings encourage you.

Actionable: Look up all debt accounts and list all his and her debts in order, from smallest to largest balance.

Debt Name	Balance	*Monthly Minimum	*Monthly Payment	How Far Behind?
Totals				

*Note the difference between *Monthly Minimum* and *Monthly Payment*. You could be paying more (or less) than the required monthly minimum. Record any differences.

Actionable Continued: The Debt Snowball Method

Eliminating debt is a great first step in the right financial direction. In fact, it's usually the key to unlocking the true power of your financial plan. Attacking your debt together is a great way for you and your partner to team up and get on the same page. And the less debt you have, the more money you'll have to make even more progress in other areas.

Paying off multiple debts – in order from smallest balance to largest – is the best method to see and feel progress. But not numerically the best. costs you more than the avalanche method

Debt Snowball Instructions:

1. Get current on any debts that you are behind on.
2. Pay the minimum on all debts except the one with the smallest balance.
3. Pay as much as you can on that debt until it has been paid off.
4. Hug.
5. Apply the amount you were paying on that debt to the next largest debt (the new smallest balance).
6. Repeat until all debts have been paid off.
7. Hug again while jumping up and down. (It's possible, practice now so you know what you're doing when the time comes.)

As each debt is paid off, the amount you are paying on the new smallest debt will increase dramatically. This allows each debt to be paid off faster and faster, thus the phrase *debt snowball.*

Better Conversations: Debt and your relationship:

How do you feel about the total amount of debt you owe?
It is a lot of money but we can comfortably make the payments right now. So I dont feel too bad about it. If one of us were to stop working, however, things would be tight.

How did you feel about those monthly payments before doing this worksheet?

How do you feel now that you have modified them using the debt snowball?
I have no interest in this method at this time.

How can you both take ownership over each other's debts?

How does referring to each other's debt as "our debt" feel?

What is your comfort level with taking on new debt in the future? Discuss any differences. (Or hug again if you don't have any!) I am fine with taking on more debt so long as it goes toward the purchase of cash flowing assets.

How aggressive do you want to be when it comes to paying off debt? Discuss any differences. (That's enough hugging for now.)
I would rather focus on building investments that will create a greater long term return. However, I am open to going for the aggressive debt reduction route if that is something we want to do together. We could probably pay off all student loans in around 3 years. If we really focused on it. Less if we ↑ our income.

How will you feel when you start making more progress paying off your debt?

How will it feel to be totally debt free? How will that change your life for the better? What will it enable you to do? If all my student loans were paid off it would free up significant cashflow to be able to invest into building our future. Real estate investing would involve further debt however.

How can viewing your debt as "ours" help grow, deepen, and strengthen your relationship? What kind of problems does "keeping score" on each other's debt bring about?

Motivation:

Paying off debt has a guaranteed ROI.

Paying off debt has a stronger return than any investment you make. I'll say that again. It pays more to pay off your debt than to invest in any other financial opportunity. Most investments have ups and downs, but paying off debt works out *every single time.* **There is no down side to paying off debt. It's always a winning decision.**

I would greatly debate this. It does offer somewhat better security, but less long-term wealth and fewer options.

Therefore, creating a plan to pay off debt is arguably the best use of time when organizing your finances.

When you look at your list of debts (You filled out the Debt Destruction chart, right?), what would you rather be doing with those monthly payments?

Investing to build up income streams that will allow me to spend more time with family, travel, and volunteering in the future.

This question could either sting a little, or open your eyes, or both. Either way, I hope it helps motivate you to pay off your debt as fast as possible.

Depending on the amount of debt you have, you could be in for a very long hike up a very steep mountain. It might help to see paying off your debt as a (fun-ish) challenge rather than a punch to the gut. Stay positive, you can do this! It will be worth it. And yes, there is an end in sight, a day when you will be completely debt free.

You can still enjoy the rest of your money (and your life) while paying off debt. Focus on the positives of paying off your debt instead of the decisions that brought debt into your life. Don't delay happiness until you make that final payment – find inexpensive ways to enjoy time with each other, and talk about your hopes and dreams for the future.

Teaming up and attacking your new enemy together will draw you closer together. Focus all your energy on destroying your debt as fast as you can. This should be an energy-giving process, not one that drains you.

Make Debt Destruction your new hobby! Get excited about the process – and the pay off.

2 Assets: All the Money in One Place

I hope you're wearing your favorite undies because it's about to get hot in here. (Hey, we are all married adults here, it's okay.)

Laying yourself bare financially is exposing. And it can be uncomfortable at first, especially if you have been keeping your finances covered up. Inviting your spouse into your financial world eventually improves your sense of oneness, too. And that trumps any awkward feelings you may have at the beginning.

Actionable: List all his and her liquid assets.

Liquid assets include accounts that are purely financial. Cash, savings, checking, IRA, 401k, mutual funds, stocks, bonds, even coins in the car's ash tray.

Do *not* include the value of your house, cars, or vinyl record collection. We will talk about how to include "stuff" as assets when we calculate your net worth.

Asset Name	Value in dollars
Total	$

Better Conversation$: Assets

How do you feel about the total amount of liquid assets you own?

Happy with the progress that has been made. started 2016 with almost $0 and now built up to

Do you feel comfortable claiming ownership over each other's assets?

How does referring to each other's assets as "our assets" feel?

Are you hesitant to claim your spouse's assets as your own?

No

Are you hesitant to "share" your assets with your spouse?

No

Do financial assets translate into feelings of security and safety for you? Discuss with each other how so. Having cash on hand is very comforting. knowing that I won't be desperate for money if an unexpected expense comes in is huge to me.

What expectations do you have for saving, investing, and growing assets?

I want to put at least 20% of each pay check into investing. I would love to get to the point where Judy and I can live off of one income and save/invest the rest.

Do your expectations line up with each others?

What expectations do you have for the amount of total assets you wish to have in the near and distant future? I need to calculate out our financial freedom number. My goal is to hit that by age 40 at the latest

How can viewing your assets as "ours" help grow, deepen, and strengthen your relationship?

Motivational:

A million dollars is saved one dollar at a time, not ten-thousand dollars at a time. It's a slow and steady process. If saving a large amount of money is one of your goals, you can do it. Take it one step at a time.

Even if it takes twelve or forty-eight months to start putting more cash towards savings, it will be worth it and it's very doable. You will find more margin to include saving in your monthly budget as you complete this finance-organization process.

If saving money feels more like a dream than a reality, be encouraged by these truths.

-When you pay off your debt, the amount you can save will increase.
-When you organize a monthly budget, you will find "extra" money that you can save.
-When you get a raise, you can increase the amount you invest.
-When you reduce your spending and cut out monthly expenses, you can increase the amount of money you invest.
-When you agree on a plan, you'll feel better about your future, your relationship, and your finances.

All signs point towards continual improvement and an increased ability to move in the right direction.

Better days with bigger bank accounts are just around the corner!

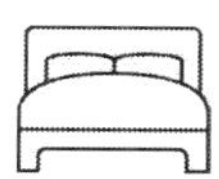

3 The Same Shoebox

Actionable: Fill in the blanks to see your combined financial big picture.

As you can see, we are separating his and hers and then combining everything into "ours." We will discuss why after the numbers are filled in. For now, let it be a little awkward. (Hug as needed.)

Income

His net monthly income	Her net monthly income	Our net monthly income

Debt

His total debt balance	Her total debt balance	Our total debt balance

Assets (Liquid assets only)

His total assets	Her total assets	Our total assets

Same shoebox continued...

We temporarily separated everything for a reason. (Not only to make things awkward!)

Talk through any feelings of financial lopsidedness. We can't simply combine money and expect any feelings of unfairness to magically disappear.

Approach this topic delicately. Very delicately. Having more or less assets than your spouse is not a reflection on your worth as a person. Nor does it determine your position of power within the relationship.

It can be easy to tie up your emotions and self-worth in a number – whether it be positive or negative. Keep this in mind as you discuss the different amounts you and your spouse bring to the table. And remember that he or she may be more sensitive to this issue than you are.

It's understandable to resist taking ownership of each other's debts and assets. It's also understandable to feel uneasy about bringing financial baggage into your spouse's world.

Being the one to "benefit" financially comes with it's own set of challenges. Often, the partner with less assets will feel like they are bringing their partner down. Trust me, that can be very difficult. It's important to work through these feelings together.

Then we put all our cash into the same shoebox.

Combining everything on paper signifies the very real financial oneness that you are aiming for in your relationship. Numbers on a sheet of paper are one thing but taking complete ownership over each other's finances is the true goal.

Combining bank accounts could be the strangest thing you've done in your relationship yet. (Well, second strangest, depending on how your honeymoon went.)

But seriously, who is that stranger in your bedroom and why are you sharing your hard-earned money with them all of a sudden? (And why on Earth are you suddenly responsible for paying off *his* student loans?) Standing in front of each other in your financial underwear is awkward at best, but the results of the process are worth it.

Better Conversations: The Same Shoebox

How do you feel about combining all of your finances?

How has this process so far helped you to feel closer to each other?

What feelings still need to be worked through to bring you to a place of feeling even closer together?

Are there any hesitations or concerns that need to be addressed before moving on? (Now is the time.)

How can you work through and be okay with any inequalities in your individual income, debt, spending habits, and savings? If your answer is, “He needs to change,” put down this workbook, pick up the book version of *One Bed, One Bank Account*, and read the chapter called Training Your Marriage.

Motivational: Same shoe box

Holding onto any financial inequality grudges is something that you'll want to drop quickly.

Equal income, debt, assets, saving and spending isn't what we are looking for anyway. If forcing financial equality is the goal, we have set ourselves up for constant failure. Equal isn't the point. The point is to let this process enrich your relationship no matter how the numbers look.

The fact that things will be financially un-balanced is the very reason that we get to work through this process of combining finances. It's bigger than just adding and subtracting numbers. We get to dive deeper and move beyond trying to make things equal. If it was all equal all the time, we might not be learning, stretching, and growing as much as we are.

Let go of any frustrations and embrace oneness.

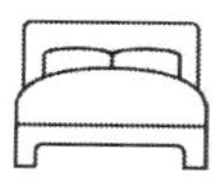

4 Our Net Worth

Actionable: Subtract your total debt from your total assets to calculate your net worth. Use the same numbers from the previous pages.

Our Total Assets ___________________________________

Minus -

Our Total Debt ___________________________________

Equals =

Our Net Worth ___________________________________

Better Conversations: Relational net worth

From this point forward, and forever more, your money is "married" – on paper and in your mindset! Maybe one day soon your money can have little baby-monies! (No joke, growing your assets with investments will bring more money into your growing family!)

Does putting all your money in the same shoebox give you a sense of togetherness or is all this still awkward? Talk with each other about how you are feeling.

What expectations do you have for growing your net worth?

How quickly would you like to grow your net worth?

If your net worth is negative, is turning it around important to you? Why?

If growing your net worth is important to you, what ideas do you have for moving in that direction?

Would another hug help?

Motivational: Net Worth

Calculating your net worth together each month is a great way to see your financial situation in its most simplistic terms. It's just *one* number!

It's also a great way to see *progress.*

If your net worth is negative, you are not alone.

A negative net worth doesn't necessarily mean you are making poor choices. The book, and this workbook, are about helping you look ahead to the future. We aren't going to spend much time revisiting the past.

You can track a negative net worth in the same way you would track a positive one. Seeing your net worth get closer to a positive number each month can be incredibly motivating, even addicting!

We post our budget and net worth on our website every month. If you're curious, feel free to take a look here:

www.derekandcarrie.com/networth

There you will also find a link to a huge list of other people who post their budget and net worth online. (Some positive, some negative.)

Go ahead, take a look!

You aren't alone in this fight. Think about it. Everyone is fighting the same financial fight. We just don't see it. Sometimes peering into the world of those with a similar situation can help. Peering into the world of someone with a situation that you are aiming for can help too!

Counting (or not counting) the house and the car.

Some people choose to count a mortgage as debt but then do *not* count the value of the house as an asset. (Same with cars.)

Reason being...

If you sell your house, chances are you will purchase another house and simply "transfer" the cash value of the house *immediately* back into the new home you purchase. The cash value of the house is unavailable to be used elsewhere. (If you make a profit on the transaction, you can then add the extra cash to your net worth. It has become *liquid.)*

Think of the cash value of a house as a sunk expense that you never get back (even if you own the house!) In other words, you will never get to use the cash value (equity) of your home for anything other than buying another home, so why count it as part of your assets/net worth?

If you listed a mortgage as a debt, you could go back and list the value of your home as an asset to see how it changes your net worth. Doing so will give you a drastically different picture of your net worth. You just need to remember that the cash value of your house is frozen.

Same with the cars

Listing a car note as a debt but *not* listing the value of the car as an asset gives a different (and some would say more accurate) picture of your net worth too. Like a house, when you sell a car you will most likely use the cash to immediately purchase another car. If you make a cash profit from the sale of a car, simply add the cash to your net worth.

The value of your house and your cars are “un-available assets” that you shouldn’t think of in the same way as you do liquid (cash) assets. You can’t use part of your house or car to buy food, only cash will do that!

Calculate your net worth with and without the value of your cars and your home as assets to see your financial situation from two very different perspectives.

It’s up to you how you choose to calculate your net worth. Doing it both ways is best to better understand your financial situation. Understand the difference and then pick the way that works best for you.

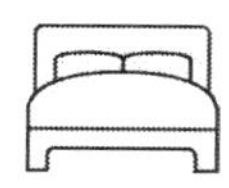

5A Short-term Cash Savings

Stuff happens. Let's plan for it.

Actionable: Divide your savings among all the items you are saving for.

The amount of cash you *currently* have saved for medium sized purchases (between 2 and 10 years) is $____________________________. Allocate this amount among all the items you list below. (Suggested list on next page.)

Item	Allocated Savings Amount (dollars)
Total Savings	

Short-term savings suggested list:

Include all mid-range non-monthly purchases that you will need in the next 2 - 10 years.

- New car(s) including all registration fees
- Major car repairs like new tires and transmission
- Vacation
- Replacement furniture
- School/education
- New computer
- New cell phone
- Home repairs (new roof, garage door opener, windows, driveway work)
- Funeral travel and expenses
- Washer/Dryer
- Hot water heater
- Another cell phone 'cause you dropped that other one in that hole in the sidewalk
- Hanson reunion concert tickets (Actually, Carrie just informed me that they never broke up and still tour to this day. Who knew!?)

Better Conversations: Short-term savings

How far did your savings stretch? Did it cover everything?

Are there any expenses that you aren't able to cover? What are they?

What ideas do you have for creating a plan to be able to cover more of these items?

Will you need to rearrange your savings plan to better prioritize your savings goals?

Did any light bulbs go off while filling out this worksheet?

Why can't we ever get ahead?

A leading cause of continual financial stuck-ness is the lack of planning for these items. These mid-range expenses are the ones that always "sneak up on you" and rob any progress you've made.

If you are having trouble getting and staying on top of your expenses, what are a few things that would help (e.g. getting a raise, finding a new job with higher earning potential, spending less on restaurants, etc.)? Get creative!

Expenses like these are almost as certain as the water bill. (That reminds me, better add emergency water main explosion to the list!)

With a plan, these expenses won't be able to sneak up on you. You'll spot them a mile off and handle them with ease.

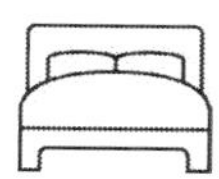

5B Short-term Savings Plan

Actionable: Create a simple plan that includes all those medium sized expenses.

Think of anything and everything you will purchase in the next 2 - 10 years and record on this list. The more items you put on this list, the more accurate the "monthly amount to save" will be and the more helpful this worksheet will be for you.

(See earlier page for suggested list. But don't stop there, keep brainstorming. There are probably a few expenses that are unique to you.)

Divide the cost of each item by the average amount of months between each purchase to uncover the monthly amount you need to save.

Example:

Item	Cost	Average numbers of months between purchase	Monthly amount to save
Car	$9,000	72	$125
Hot Water Heater	$1,000	180	$5.55
New Computer	$1,200	36	33.33
Totals	$11,200	Not needed	$163.88

Our short-term savings plan:

Item	**Cost**	**Average numbers of months between purchase**	**Monthly amount to save**
Totals		Not needed	

Instructional video at DerekAndCarrie.com/budgetlesson

Short-term savings and your relationship

Some people are planners. Some people prefer to (scratch their head and figure out how to) cross that bridge when they get to it.

Where do you fall as far as planning ahead for medium-range expenses?

Better Conversations: Short term savings

If there are differences in the way you approach short-term savings, what kind of impact are those differences having on your relationship? (And on your financial future?)

How can differences in this area be viewed as a positive thing for your relationship and your finances?

Can your strengths and weaknesses in this area be seen as helpful? How so?

Motivation

If you can cover more than half of the items on your list of future expenses, you are in great shape! Hug and have some pie.

These medium sized expenses are easy to overlook and will sneak up on you if you don't plan. They are often given the label of "unexpected," but now you know better.

The truth is we *should* expect them and can *easily* plan for them. Set yourself up for success and create a monthly savings plan to cover these medium-range expenses. We will work this into your budget on the next worksheet.

It's easy to visualize and plan for monthly bills and expenses. Even planning and saving for retirement can be easier than planning for these sneaky medium sized expenses.

Now that you guys have a plan, you'll sleep better tonight in your One Bed.
Won't that be fun?

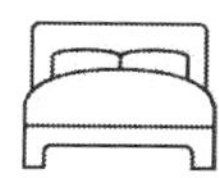

6 Monthly Budget

It's time for a better conversation about budgets. Get ready to love your budget in a borderline inappropriate manner.

Monthly budget instructions:

Step one: Last month (Travel back in time)

- Print off your bank statement(s) and any other spending statements like a credit card or student loan payment.
- Using a blank sheet of paper (or a nifty spreadsheet) put each expense into a spending category. See example categories on example budget below and modify as needed.
- Record the totals for each spending category on the budget under the Recap column. (See example budget.)

Step two: Next month (Predict the future)

- Create a new budget for the upcoming month.
- Keep in mind how much you spent last month in each category and make any necessary changes for the upcoming month.
- You have already found a monthly total for debt and medium-range savings (see previous two worksheets). You may simply record those totals in the first two rows. Don't accidentally record any debt payments twice. Just record one grand total for all your monthly debt payments as calculated on worksheet #1.

Step three: Find the difference

- Subtract the recap column from the budget column to find the difference.
- The difference represents any adjustments you need to make this month to make your budget.

Example Budget: Income

Net Income	Budget (Beginning of month)	Recap (End of month recap)	Difference
Total Income	$1,535	$ 1600	$ +65

Example Budget: Expenses

Monthly Expenses	Budget (Beginning of Month)	Recap (End of month recap)	Difference
Total debt from worksheet #1	300	300	0
Total savings from worksheet #5b	345	300	+45
Giving	100	100	0
Rent (Mortgage goes on debt total above!)	0	0	0
Grocery	300	350	-50
Restaurant	120	115	+5
Electric	90	100	-10
Gas	50	45	5
Water	40	44	-4
Internet	65	65	0
Cable	35	35	0
Cell Phone	90	100	-10
TOTALS	1535	1554	-19

Example Budget: Totals

Total Income (From the top of budget)	1535	1600	+65
Minus total expenses	1535	1554	+19
Equals (Should equal ZERO)	0	46	+46

Your New Budget: Income

Net Income	Budget (Beginning of month)	Recap (End of month recap)	Difference
Total Income	$	$	$

Your New Budget: Expenses

Monthly Expenses	Budget (Beginning of Month)	Recap (End of month recap)	Difference
Total debt from worksheet #1			
Total savings from worksheet #5b			
Giving			
Rent (Mortgage goes on debt total above!)			
Grocery			
Restaurant			
Electric			
Gas			
Water			
Internet			
Cable			
Cell Phone			

Monthly Expenses ...continued	Budget	Recap	Difference

TOTAL expenses			

Your New Budget: Totals

Total Income (From the top of budget)			
Minus Expenses (From bottom of budget			
Equals (Should equal ZERO)			

Monthly budget and your relationship

Talking for hours? Good.

Our first budget took four hours to complete. Not because our calculator wasn't working, but because of all the conversations we had along the way. (Essential oils? Seriously, I'm helping you pay for that?!)

Working your monthly budget together is a fantastic starting place for great conversations.

Some people feel right at home with a budget.
Some people see budgeting as a tedious task filled with endless amounts of stress.

How can you both play to your strengths, and weaknesses, to arrive at a common goal: a successful budget that works?

Take your time and enjoy the conversations!

Better Conversations: Monthly Budget

Did working a budget together bring up any new realizations concerning how you approach organizing and managing your money?

Name, and talk about, one specific area of your budget each that you feel needs to be addressed.

How does the budgeting process feel? Is it making good sense or would some more practice help? Discuss.

How can a budget bring more freedom and confidence into your financial life?

Name two things you learned to appreciate about your mate from these discussions.

Does anything about your attitude, expectations, and actions need attention?

Motivation

First time budgeting? It takes a minimum of four months to get a good handle on how budgeting works. It also takes four months to see real changes. (It's worth it, trust me!)

Lots of people choose to print off a blank budget and fill it in by hand the first several months. After you get a good feel for how it works you can start using spreadsheets or an online app. Choose the budgeting method that works best for you.

A life-long process

Do a budget every month for one year and you won't believe the progress you can make!

Budgeting is just like working out. It gets easier the more you do it, but still takes discipline. Once it becomes a habit, the results multiply.

Your budget will become more useful and accurate as each month goes by. Some people find that they accidentally leave out a few expenses the first time they work a budget. Once you discover them, add them in for a more complete budget.

A budget is like a big math problem with a lot of moving parts, each part is needed in order to work properly. Leaving out big chunks will make it feel like the budget isn't working right. The budget works just fine, it just needs all the right info to do its job well.

The best way to create a budget is to jump in and learn as you go. It won't be perfect or pretty the first time, but it will get easier each month.

Remember that you have access to the video instructional series at:
derekandcarrie.com/budgetlesson

The video series covers how each worksheet works. It also includes links to dozens of helpful budgeting resources... and just maybe there's a video of us hugging and jumping.

It's all about the money. (Except for all the way-more-important things, like your relationship.)

Working on your money together is supposed to bring you closer together. Yes, really.

This workbook isn't only about the math and spreadsheets, it's about growing closer through the process.

Your financial goals can bring you together as a couple no matter how messy, or squeaky clean, the situation happens to be.

If your net worth is sky-rocketing, great! I hope your relationship is sky-rocketing too.

Struggling through this process *together* can strengthen your relationship too. (Remember our financial-disaster story in the book?) Getting your teeth kicked in is never fun, but going through tough times with someone else can create lasting bonds of trust and confidence.

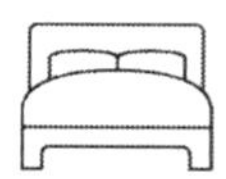

7 Cutting The Cord

We all have them. Small (or sometimes big) items that we can't help but buy when given the chance. For me, it's pastries. And coffee. And when Carrie's not looking, Reeses peanut butter cups. These are all small purchases, but when added up over months, they can have a real effect on our budget (and my waistline, but that's another book).

Actionable: List all monthly *impulse* purchases.
(Soda, coffee, snacks, clothes, skateboards, jet-ski.)

Decide together if you are going to keep it, reduce it, or eliminate it.

Impulse buy	Keep	Eliminate or reduce by $_________	Action step needed to reduce or eliminate
		$	
		$	
		$	
		$	
		$	
		$	
		$	
Total		$	

How much did you save by reducing or eliminating a few impulse buys?

$ _______________________

Monthly bills, impulse buys and your relationship

Small impulse buys no longer affect only you, like they did when you were single.

When you order *another* season of Friends DVDs, so does your spouse. And when your spouse is out spending money all over town, so are you, even though you are at home watching Friends!

Listing out monthly bills and impulse buys encourages you to really consider each expense – together. Seeing these expenses listed out gives a better picture of how much money is being spent. Once you see where your money is going you can make changes where needed.

As you consider reducing or eliminating each expense, your mind will open up to new and creative alternatives – and financial-lifestyle choices.

If you never question these day-to-day expenses, your mind will likely never open up to new possibilities. Why would it, if you never consider it?

Give yourself a monthly allowance

One easy way to handle impulse buys within a relationship: agree on a set amount for "his" and "hers" spending cash.

Example: $100 each.

Work $100 each into your monthly budget. Each person can purchase anything they want with their $100. Once the money has been spent, you are finished with impulse buys for the month. You can't buy anything else. Not even gum, garlic-breath. Okay, maybe gum, if it will save your marriage.

With this method you can plan to be impulsive. Control the impulse buys before they run wild.

Motivation

Impulse tips: *What to do when tempted.*

25/24 Rule: If it costs more than $25, wait twenty-four hours to purchase. Waiting just one day will help you determine if you really do need (or even want) the impulse buy.

Imagine you bought it (but don't): Stand in front of the item you are thinking of purchasing, hold it in your hands if you want and imagine yourself using the item. Ask yourself if buying the item is really going to improve your life. Imagine how you will feel a few hours, or a few weeks, after buying the item. Will you still care that much about it? How will you feel in a few hours or weeks if you *don't* buy it?

Substitute: Is there another way to get the same benefit, or a similar experience, some other way?

Opportunity cost: What else could you do with the money? (Perhaps that $10 could go towards paying off your credit card.)

Temporary: Pick just a few expenses each month to reduce or eliminate. Then add those back in and cut something else the next month. A monthly target can keep this process fun and keep you motivated.

You earned it: Ask yourself how much time or effort it took you to earn the money you would need to purchase the item. If it takes you a half a day to earn the money needed to make the purchase, you might reconsider buying that Friends DVD set.

You don't have to cut everything out completely to make good progress. Just cutting a few things in half, and eliminating one or two others is usually enough to see big changes.

Okay, this might be a good place for another hug.

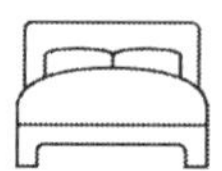

8 Live on Half

This is a helpful mind-stretching exercise that will get you thinking more analytically about your finances. It isn't possible for most couples to simply decide to live off of half of their income.

What would it take?
What would it do for your finances?
What would it do for your lifestyle expectations?

This worksheet may help you to come up with some other goals you never would have thought of. You may also find that living on half of your income is more possible than you expected.

Actionable: What would it take to live on half of your income?

Our monthly net income is $ ____

Half of our monthly income is $ ____

In order to live on half, we would have to cut out the following expenses...

Go CRAZY! This is meant to be fun and bring about creative ideas.

To live on half we would need to sell our cars, live in a cave, and grow our own food!

Expense name	Amount we spend each month	Cut by... (Half, All, Some)	Amount saved $
			$
			$
			$
			$
			$
			$
			$
			$
			$
Total			$

Living on half and your relationship:

Living on half sounds extreme but it's a reality for many couples.

When a couple has a child, and one parent stops working in order to stay home full time, *that couple is living on half!* Just think of the millions of households with a full-time stay-at-home parent. Yes, living on half is very common.

(Two people living on one income = both partners living on half of one salary.)

If these couples can make it on one income after having kids, chances are they could have done it before kids when they both had an income.

Living on half before kids looks a little different. Earning two incomes and saving one is another example of living on half.

In this case it's two incomes but the couple is living on the first income and saving all of the second income. Different – very different – but the same idea.

Living on half before having kids will establish more realistic and sustainable financial-lifestyle expectations. A side benefit is having good head start on savings!

This exercise is supposed to get you thinking in radical ways of what is possible even if you don't actually end up living on half of your household income. If you never hit half, but do hit seventy-three percent, well that's not bad, either.

Better Conversations: Living on half

How did this *live on half* exercise help you get creative with your financial-lifestyle choices?

What ideas did this exercise bring about that you will consider trying?

How does this live on half idea relate to your situation (currently and in the near future)?

What "crazy" dreams would living on half make more achievable?

Motivation:

If the idea of living on half of your income feels extreme, good! It's supposed to feel extreme.

We are stretching outside your comfort zone to explore new areas of finance and lifestyle possibilities. Most people spend all their money, no matter how much they earn, without thinking about alternative possibilities. Challenging this pattern will put you in control.

To get even more out of this exercise pretend that it *is* possible to live on half. Visualize and talk about what your life would look like if you pulled the trigger on this and arranged your lifestyle to live on half.

Cut your expenses in half on paper and discuss each change that would need to be made.

Is living on half in your future?

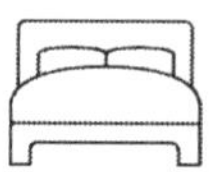

DUAL
INCOME
NO
KIDS

Are you a DINK?

If you and your partner are both earning a paycheck and there are no kids in the equation yet, you are a couple of D.I.N.K.s.

As history has proven time and time again, you will likely spend however much you make. Even when you get a raise, your spending is likely to rise up to the new level of your increased income. It's almost a given for many millions of couples.

Spending what you earn is natural, it's easy, it's the default.

You establish financial-lifestyle habits and expectations based on your combined household income before having kids. Maybe you have student loans and credit cards that you could be paying off faster. Maybe you even have a car payment that you can handle, for now.

Then you buy a house together. Not just any house. The most house you can afford! (Hey, the bank said you could afford it so it's okay, right?)

Things are okay. You are keeping your head above water.

Then you have a baby. Congratulations!

If one of you decides to stay home full time, you are looking at losing what percentage of your household income? 30%? 55%?

Or maybe you decide to both continue working. How much will childcare cost each month? Are you one of the lucky ones with Grandma three streets over who offers to babysit 50 hours a week, for free? Good for you! Can she take one more?

You get the idea. Life gets more expensive at the same time your income drops. Keeping up with all the financial obligations, habits, and expectations that you established back in the good old days when you had two incomes and no kids, gets harder and harder each month.

Here's what we suggest doing instead.

Live on half of your household income now! Seriously. Do it.

Use the other half to pay off any debt you have as fast as you possibly can.
Being debt free before kids is as close to financial Heaven on Earth as you can get!

Once you are debt free, continue to live on half and save the other half.

When your little bundle of joy comes (crashing) into your world, not only will you be debt free and have a big pile of cash savings, you will have something even better...

You will have realistic financial-lifestyle expectations, obligations, and habits that are sustainable.

It's so much easier to start and stay small than to go too big, too early, and have to downsize your lifestyle later.

Just like your health, it's easier to stay in shape than it is to get in shape.

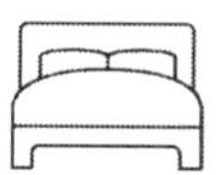

9 Five-year Plan: Paint a Picture

Creating a five-year plan helped us define how we wanted our life together to look.

A five-year plan helps create a vision that you can see and feel. Once that vision has been created it's much easier to take action and get moving.

Establishing a five-year plan also gives you something tangible to grab on to. Having a place to start and a direction to travel gets the wheels turning.

How a plan can work for you

A few years ago some of our friends were stuck.

He got laid off and couldn't find a new job.
She wasn't digging her job and really wanted to find something new.

After more than a year of nothing going their way, it was time for a change.

One day they sat down together and admitted that the lack of a vision for their life was holding them back. That afternoon they created a five-year plan and everything changed.

They asked each other, “What do we want our life together to look like?”

Everything from friends, family, jobs, and even where they wanted to live was questioned and discussed.

They decided to move to another state to kick-start their five-year plan.

Just a few months later they had moved and both had good jobs that they liked. And it was all due to taking a step back, dreaming a little, and taking action.

Five-Year Plan Instructions:

- Write down where you are now, your starting place. How does it look and feel?
- Write down where you want to be.
- Write down the first step to getting there.
- Write down the direction you need to move to get closer to your goal.

*Answers should be four sentences or less.

Paint a picture

Financial planning is a very left-brained process. Figures have to add up. Your bank account has a definitive dollar amount in it that can't be argued. Although this number is set in stone, there are many factors that generated the numbers. And most of them are emotional. You spend your money the way you do for a reason. Robots can separate emotions from money, but you are human so lets use those emotions in the best way possible.

Since the majority of the factors that created your bank balance have nothing to do with math and everything to do with how you operate, we don't want to neglect your intuitive right brain.

This is the part of the workbook where you literally draw a picture of where you want to be in five years. Don't skip this! Even if you're as left-brained as they come, you will get something out of this exercise. I was skeptical the first time I did this (during one of our birthing classes), but I was shocked by how helpful it was.

It brought to the surface things we had been feeling but didn't realize or know how to verbalize.

The rules (follow these same rules for each area you are asked to draw a picture):

1) You have to do it. No skipping. This isn't an art contest. You're the only one who needs to know what you draw. Unless it's abstract. Then no one – not even you – will ever know.
2) Focus. Think of how you want to feel, how it will be different from how you feel now. Think of the fears and concerns you have now and how you want those to change. Think of the joys you want to be experiencing in five years.
3) Draw for at least five minutes. When you think you are done, draw a little bit more. Even if you just re-trace the same smiley face over and over. (That actually sounds therapeutic. I know what I'm doing this afternoon.)
4) Show, or at least try to explain your drawing to your spouse. This exercise is mostly for your benefit, but if something exciting or unexpected comes from your drawing, be sure to share it with your spouse.

If this was especially helpful for you, add drawing time into your monthly budget process!

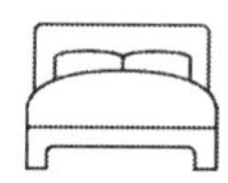

9A Financial

Where do we want to be in 5 years?

Describe the situation and include how you want to feel.

Where are we now?

Include what's good about where you are now and what you would like to change.

How are we going to get there?

Keep it simple!

What is the first step?

In what direction do we need to move?

Paint or draw a picture

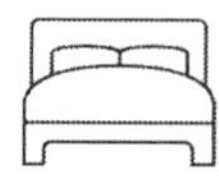

9B Health and Wellness

Where do we want to be in 5 years?

Describe the situation and include how you want to feel.

Where are we now?

Include what's good about where you are now and what you would like to change.

How are we going to get there?

Keep it simple!

What is the first step?

In what direction do we need to move?

How does money affect this area of life?

Paint or draw a picture

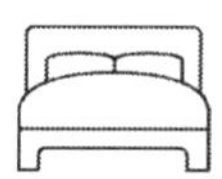

9C Spiritual

Where do we want to be in 5 years?
Describe the situation and include how you want to feel.

Where are we now?
Include what's good about where you are now and what you would like to change.

How are we going to get there?
Keep it simple!

What is the first step?

In what direction do we need to move?

Paint or draw a picture

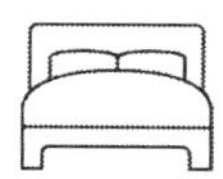

9D Personal Development

Where do we want to be in 5 years?
Describe the situation and include how you want to feel.

Where are we now?
Include what's good about where you are now and what you would like to change.

How are we going to get there?
Keep it simple!

What is the first step?

In what direction do we need to move?

How does money affect this area of life?

Paint or draw a picture

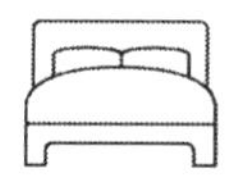

9E Family

Where do we want to be in 5 years?

Describe the situation and include how you want to feel.

Where are we now?

Include what's good about where you are now and what you would like to change.

How are we going to get there?

Keep it simple!

What is the first step?

In what direction do we need to move?

How does money affect this area of life?

Paint or draw a picture

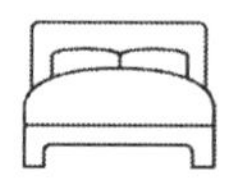

9F Friends / Social

Where do we want to be in 5 years?

Describe the situation and include how you want to feel.

Where are we now?

Include what's good about where you are now and what you would like to change.

How are we going to get there?

Keep it simple!

What is the first step?

In what direction do we need to move?

How does money affect this area of life?

Paint or draw a picture

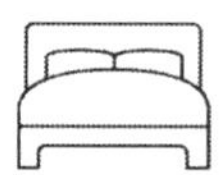

The Horizon

Let's bring it in for a landing, shall we?

All you really need is a plan.

A plan that gives you confidence.
A plan that allows you to focus.
A plan that leads to action.

So many of the financial messes I see are a result of lack of planning.
But now you have a plan, a good one. One that will take you in the right direction.

You guys are a team.
You are in this together.

If you crash and burn, do it together.
If you save a billion dollars, do it together.

Let your financial ups and downs bring you together.

There are problems in life that you solve and there are problems in life that you manage.

Money is a part of life that you *manage.*
Treating money like a problem you are supposed to solve and never revisit leads to all kinds of frustration.

You'll be managing money for as long as you are on this Earth.
Let the journey strengthen your relationship.

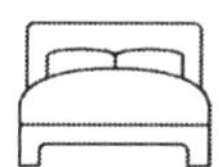

Epilogue

I'm actually not sure if this is an epilogue, but we always wanted to write one.

We have some questions for you.

First, did you and your mate do all the exercises in this workbook? How did you do?

We want to remind you that this is a *process*. Better conversations take time, and sometimes involve some not-so-great talks, arguments, and emotional explosions. Been there. Last week. Will be there again. Next week.

If you get stuck, we recommend going through the book again. (Not this workbook, the book. The one you read first, right?)

Also - Subscribe to our podcast. We keep it fun, practical, and around twenty minutes.

Oh, and our email newsletter. All this fun, free stuff at www.DerekAndCarrie.com.

While you're there, feel free to send us questions. Yes, we answer them, and use your feedback to create better podcasts and blogs... which helps other couples... and the circle of awesomeness continues.

Thank you for investing in these resources, and for your support!

We would love to hear from you. Please consider leaving a review of this workbook on Amazon: http://www.derekandcarrie.com/amazon.

Thank you.

–Derek and Carrie

ABOUT DEREK AND CARRIE

Derek and Carrie encourage couples to have better conversation on money. It was these types of conversations that allowed Derek and Carrie to survive financial disaster early in their marriage. When they aren't touring the country in their travel trailer, they live in Kansas City with their daughter, Amelie.

Derek and Carrie are available for speaking engagements and media appearances. Please visit DerekAndCarrie.com/press for more info.

BONUS GOAL SETTING WORKSHEET:

Goal setting:

- Write the goal down
- Set a realistic deadline
- Identify any challenges or obstacles that stand in your way
- Contact any people or organizations that you need to work with
- Write down how reaching the goal will feel
- Develop a plan of action
- What do we need to accomplish this year?
    - This Quarter?
    - This Month?
    - This week?
    - Today?
- Take the first step
- Focus your time, efforts, and energy
- Make progress everyday

Additional Resources

Book

One Bed, One Bank Account: Better Conversations on Money and Marriage
Book and audio book available at
DerekAndCarrie.com/products

Podcast

Better Conversations on Money and Marriage
Listen and subscribe at
DerekAndCarrie.com/listen

Instructional video series

Access videos at DerekAndCarrie.com/budgetlesson

YouTube!

Epic Adventures happening right now at DerekAndCarrie.com/video

Newsletter

Sign up for our newsletter at DerekAndCarrie.com

NOTES

NOTES

NOTES

NOTES

NOTES

Made in the USA
Lexington, KY
18 May 2017